W9-CDA-158

FLEETWAY

D.R. & QUINCH

ALAN
MOORE

ALAN
DAVIS

DEFINITIVE EDITIONS

3 **D.R. & QUINCH** *Have Fun on Earth*

10 **D.R. & QUINCH** *Go Straight*

21 **D.R. & QUINCH** *Go Girl Crazy*

36 **D.R. & QUINCH** *Get Drafted*

62 **D.R. & QUINCH** *Go to Hollywood*

88 **D.R. & QUINCH** *Get Back to Nature*

MANAGING DIRECTOR
JON DAVIDGE

U.S. SALES DIRECTORS
SAL QUARTUCCIO
BOB KEENAN

MANAGING EDITOR
STEVE MacMANUS

GRAPHIC ALBUM EDITOR
STEVE EDGELL

DESIGN
COLIN FOX

Cover illustration by *Alan Davis*
Interior coloring created by *Lurene Haines*
Definitive Editions produced by *Bob Keenan* and *Sal Quartuccio*

Published by Fleetway Publications, Greater London House, Hampstead Road, London NWI 7QQ, a member of Maxwell Consumer Publishing & Communication Ltd. U.K. Distribution and Export by MacDonald & Co (Publishers) Ltd, Tel (071) 377 4600. US Representation and Marketing: SQP Inc, PO Box 4569, Toms River, New Jersey 08754, USA. Sole US Distributor: Titan Distributors, 205 41st Street, Brooklyn, NY 11232, USA. No similarity between any of the names, characters, persons, and/or institutions in this book with those of any living or dead person is intended, and any such similarity which may exist is purely coincidental. Printed in Spain by Cronion SA, Barcelona. Copyright © 1991 Fleetway Publications. All rights reserved. First edition August 1991. ISBN I 85386 255 X.

THARG'S TIME TWISTERS

MY NAME'S ERNIE QUINCH, COLLEGE STUDENT. I LIKE GUNS AND STARTING FIGHTS. MY PSYCHIATRIST SAYS I'M A PSYCHOTIC DEVIANT.

BUT THAT DOESN'T MEAN I'M A BAD PERSON, RIGHT?

MY BEST FRIEND IS WALDO DOBBS, ONLY EVERYBODY CALLS HIM "D.R." WHICH STANDS FOR "DIMINISHED RESPONSIBILITY". HE CAME TO COLLEGE LAST TERM, FROM REFORM SCHOOL.

IT WAS THE SUMMER OF '315 AND WE'D BEEN SUSPENDED FROM COLLEGE BECAUSE DEAN FUSK FOUND ALL THE FUR-COATS AND LASERS HIDDEN IN MY LOCKER AND CALLED THE COPS, THE DIRTBALL.

WHICH IS WHY WE'D FELT COMPELLED TO BORROW HIS CRED-CHIPS, RENT A TIME-FLIVVER AND ZOOM BACK INTO THE PREHISTORY OF THIS UTTERLY WORTHLESS FILTH-PIT PLANET CALLED EARTH.

IT WAS ALL PART OF OUR REVENGE SCHEME, AS DETAILED IN THE FOLLOWING BLOCKBUSTER STORY WHICH IS TOTALLY AMAZING AND WELL-WRITTEN AND EVERYTHING. I CALL THIS EPIC...

D.R. AND QUINCH HAVE FUN ON EARTH!

2000 A.D.
Credit Card:

SCRIPT ROBOT
E.E. QUINCH

ART ROBOT
ALAN DAVIS

LETTERING ROBOT
STEVE POTTER

COMPU·73e

VISITING EARTH WAS D.R.'S IDEA. IN HIS OPINION IT WAS A DESPICABLE SCUM-HOLE OUT IN THE BOONDOCKS AND NO-BODY REALLY *CARED* MUCH WHAT HAPPENED TO IT.

WHICH WAS JUST AS WELL, THE WAY THINGS TURNED OUT.

AFTER STOPPING IN THE *MESOZOIC ERA* TO *ZAP* A FEW LIZARDS WE SCOOTED BACK TO WHEN THE PLANET'S CRUST WAS JUST FORMING, WHICH WAS, LIKE, UNBELIEVABLY *DULL*.

LUCKILY, D.R. HAD BROUGHT A *THERMO-NUCLEAR BAZOOKA* AND A CRATE OF SHELLS.

PRETTY SOON WE HAD THE MAJOR CONTINENTAL LAND MASSES BLASTED INTO THE KINDA *SHAPE* WE WANTED, AND THE SEA WAS AS RADIOACTIVE AS THE *PHI-DELTA FRAT HOUSE,* WHICH WE *NUKED* LAST WINTER...

BTHOOM!

AFTER THAT WE PULLED OVER IN THE *LATE PRE-CAMBRIAN* AND CHECKED OUT ALL THE STUFF THAT WAS STARTING TO WRIGGLE ABOUT IN THE RADIOACTIVE MUD. IT WAS INCREDIBLY DISGUSTING.

BUT THEN, LIKE D.R. SAID, *"THAT'S LIFE."*

WE LEFT 'EM TO EVOLVE INTO SOMETHING LESS GROSS AND HEADED FOR THE PLEISTOCENE PERIOD TO SEE HOW THEY'D TURNED OUT.

I SHOWED 'EM HOW TO *HIT* EACH OTHER WITH BITS OF BONE AND THEN WE SAT BACK AND WATCHED THEM PULVERISE THEMSELVES.

D.R. SAID THAT THIS WAS A REALLY PROFOUND SCIENTIFIC THING CALLED "SURVIVAL OF THE FITTEST." PERSONALLY, I THOUGHT IT WAS JUST FUNNY.

WE DROPPED IN ON THE SURVIVORS DURING THE PALAEOLITHIC ERA AND WERE COMPLETELY DEVASTATED TO FIND THAT THERE STILL WASN'T A DECENT RESTAURANT ANYWHERE.

I GOT ONE OF THE LOCAL GUYS TO PAINT MY PICTURE. I THOUGHT IT LOOKED PRETTY AMAZING, BUT D.R. SAYS THIS PRIMITIVE STUFF IS ON THE WAY OUT.

WELL, BY THEN THEY'D DEVELOPED INTO NEANDER-THALS, WHICH WERE, LIKE, THESE OUTRAGEOUSLY STUPID, DEFORMED-LOOKING ANIMALS.

ANYWAY, WE HAD TO MOVE ON BECAUSE WE HAD LOTS OF STUFF TO DO WHICH WAS ALL PART OF OUR BRILLIANT REVENGE PLAN ON DEAN FUSK, IF YOU REMEMBER.

OUR NEXT STOP WAS ANCIENT EGYPT.

WE TRIED TO EXPLAIN ABOUT SPACE TRAVEL TO THE LOCALS, BUT THEY GOT IT ALL WRONG AND THOUGHT WE WANTED THEM TO BUILD US ALL THESE HORRIBLE POINTED BUILDINGS. TOO BAD.

WE DECIDED TO GIVE UP ON THE SPACE TRAVEL LESSONS UNTIL LATER, BECAUSE THERE WERE STILL A FEW ALTERATIONS TO MAKE TO THE PLANET'S SURFACE.

FWHOOM!

WE PARKED IN 1883 AND I TOOK OUT KRAKATOA WITH THE BAZOOKA. ACTUALLY, I ONLY MEANT TO PUT A COUPLE OF HOLES IN IT BUT I USED THE WRONG CALIBRE SHELL. NICE FLASH, THOUGH...

THEN WE HAD TO GO BACK IN TIME TO TAKE CARE OF SOME OTHER STUFF. WE SPOTTED THIS BOAT AND D.R. WANTED TO CHECK IT OUT IN CASE THERE WAS A GOOD MOVIE SHOWING.

IT WAS THE PITS. NO WONDER EVERYBODY KEPT JUMPING OVER THE SIDE...

THE MAIN THING ON OUR AGENDA WAS FIXING THESE CHIMPS UP WITH A DECENT SPACE PROGRAMME. D.R. BOUNCED SOME FRUIT OFF THIS GUY NEWTON'S HEAD UNTIL HE GOT THE IDEA ABOUT GRAVITY.

THEN, WHEN THEY FINALLY MANAGED TO GET UP INTO THE AIR, WE TRIED TO GRAB A COUPLE OF THEIR PLANES WITH THE TRACTOR BEAM, TO LOOK AT WHILE WE WERE CRUISING JUST OFF BERMUDA.

BUT THEY WERE, LIKE, REALLY INFERIOR MERCHANDISE, AND THEY, LIKE, FELL TO BITS.

THE NEXT STEP WAS TO GIVE THESE FEEBS THE IDEA OF GETTING INTO SPACE. WE ARRANGED A WHOLE BUNCH OF 'CLOSE ENCOUNTERS', MOSTLY IN THE 1950s.

WE'D STOP A CAR OR SOMETHING AND THEN D.R. WOULD WALK UP AND DOWN WITH THE WATER-COOLER ON HIS HEAD AND TALK ABOUT THE INTERSTELLAR BROTHERHOOD.

HE MADE IT ALL UP ON THE SPOT. TOTALLY AMAZING. I TRIED IT MYSELF A COUPLE OF TIMES BUT KEPT GETTING THE GIGGLES.

IT MUST HAVE WORKED, BECAUSE BY THE TIME WE PULLED INTO 1969 THESE REALLY INFERIOR CHARACTERS HAD MANAGED TO GET AS FAR AS THE MOON.

ONE SMALL STEP...

THE BANANA PEEL WAS MY IDEA. I GUESS THEY EDITED IT OUT OF THE FILM.

THE PLANET'S SURFACE STILL WASN'T EXACTLY RIGHT SO WE ZIPPED AHEAD TO 1991 AND KNOCKED A CHUNK OFF OF AMERICA BY USING A SEISMIC CANNON ON THE SAN ANDREAS FAULT.

BRAKARUMM!

BY THE TIME WE GOT BACK TO OUR OWN ERA, 3017 BY THE CHIMPS' RECKONING, THEY WERE OUT IN SPACE AND HAD ENCOUNTERED THEIR FIRST REAL, ACTUAL PEOPLE.

IT WAS EMBARRASSING. THEY WENT ON HOLOVISION AND LOOKED ALL AWE-STRUCK AND RECITED D.R.'S INTERSTELLAR BROTHERHOOD SPEECH. NOBODY KNEW WHERE TO LOOK.

SO, OF COURSE, THERE HAD TO BE A FULL CIVIC RECEPTION AT THE LEAGUE OF DISADVANTAGED PLANETS' CHARITY HALL, FOR THESE MINDLESS LIFE-FORMS.

DEAN FUSK AND HIS FAMILY ALWAYS TALKED ABOUT HOW MUCH THEY CONTRIBUTED TO THE LEAGUE, SO, LIKE, WE KNEW THEY'D BE THERE.

ME AND D.R. GOT A SEAT RIGHT BEHIND THE DEAN, HIS WIFE AND KID, STARING AT THE BACK OF HIS FAT, BLUE CENTRAVIAN NECK.

THEN THEY FINALLY GOT TO THE BIT IN THE CEREMONY WHERE THEY PROJECTED UP A HOLO-PIC OF THE NEWCOMERS' PLANET, LIKE THEY ALWAYS DO.

WHEN THE AUDIENCE SAW HOW ME AND D.R. HAD FIXED UP THE GEOGRAPHY, EVERYBODY WAS, LIKE, UTTERLY WIPED OUT.

THE SHAPE OF THE CONTINENTS IN THE NORTHERN HEMISPHERE NOW SPELLED OUT "DEAN FUSK IS EMBEZZLING THE CANTEEN FUND" IN CENTRAVIAN...

...WHILE THE SOUTHERN HEMISPHERE READ "AND MRS FUSK IS A CONVICTED SHOPLIFTER AND THEIR HORRIBLY UGLY SON MARK IS A KNOWN SNITCH."

NATURALLY, THE LEAGUE OF PLANETS ORDERED THAT THIS EARTH PLACE BE ATOMIZED RIGHT AWAY BECAUSE OF THIS TOTALLY MIND-BOGGLING GEOGRAPHIC INSULT TO ONE OF ITS MEMBERS.

THIS WAS GREAT, BECAUSE IT WIPED OUT ALL THE EVIDENCE OF OUR MESSING AROUND, LIKE ALL THE BEER CANS WE DUMPED IN THE DURASSIC PERIOD.

DEAN FUSK SORTA WENT TO PIECES AFTER THAT.

ME AND D.R. TOLD OUR SUSPENSION HEARING THAT HE WAS A CRIMINAL TYPE AND THAT HE'D PLANTED THOSE FURS AND LASERS IN MY LOCKER, AND THEY LET US BACK IN SCHOOL.

IT WAS THE BEST SUMMER I EVER HAD, PRETTY WELL, AND IF ALL KIDS FOUND SOMETHING INTERESTING TO DO INSTEAD OF HANGING ROUND CAUSING TROUBLE, IT'D BE A BETTER GALAXY.

WRITTEN BY ERNEST ERROL QUINCH, STUDENT. 63.14.'315.

The End

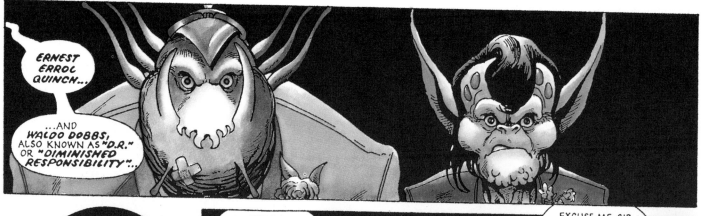

ERNEST
ERROL
QUINCH...

...AND
WALDO DOBBS,
ALSO KNOWN AS "D.R."
OR "DIMINISHED
RESPONSIBILITY"...

YOU ARE
CHARGED WITH
ARSON, KIDNAPPING,
THEFT, GRIEVOUS
WOUNDING, POSSESSION
OF UNLAWFUL
ATOMIC
WEAPONS...

...TAKING
AND DRIVING
AWAY, CONSPIRACY
TO OVERTHROW THE
GOVERNMENT,
COVETTING THY
NEIGHBOUR'S OX,
GRAVEROBBING...

...TORTURE,
CRIMINAL LIBEL,
BLACKMAIL,
POLLUTING THE
ENVIRONMENT...

EXCUSE ME, SIR,
BUT WHAT IS THE
APPELLATION OF
THIS COMPLETE AND
UTTER JUDICIAL
DIRTWAD?

WUH?

...SHOPLIFTING,
714 SEPARATE
DRIVING OFFENCES,
FORGING SACRED
RELICS...

THE JUDGE. I'D
LIKE TO MAKE A NOTE
OF HIS NAME.

OH. IT'S JUDGE
THORKWUNS.

...TRANSMUTING
BASE METAL INTO
GOLD, GENOCIDE,
SPITTING...

T-H-O-R-K-
W-U-N-G.

THANKEW.

...AND
THIRTY-TWO
OFFENCES SO
UNUSUAL AND
HORRIBLE THAT
THEY DO NOT
HAVE NAMES.

BEFORE I PASS
SENTENCE, IS THERE
ANYTHING THAT YOU
WISH TO SAY?

9

HMMM... PERHAPS YOU **SHOULD** BE GIVEN A SECOND CHANCE TO DEMONSTRATE A SHRED OF **DECENCY**...

REPORT BACK HERE IN A MONTH WITH PROOF THAT YOU HAVE PERFORMED HONEST AND CHARITABLE WORK IN THE INTERVENING TIME...

...AND WE'LL SEE ABOUT REDUCING YOUR SENTENCES BY A CENTURY OR SO. **CASE ADJOURNED!**

MY NAME IS WALDO DOBBS, AND WITH THESE WORDS I COMMENCED MY MOST TOTALLY GROTESQUE REVENGE PLOT OF ALL TIME...

"AFTER THE COURT SESSION, MY GREAT FRIEND ERNEST QUINCH AND I BEGAN OUR MODEL CITIZENSHIP WITH A VISIT TO THE LIBRARY.

"THIS WAS UNBELIEVABLY INSTRUCTIVE AND EDUCATING, AND ALL KIDS SHOULD DO IT **REGULARLY**.

"I PERSONALLY DISCOVERED NOT ONLY THE ADDRESS OF JUDGE THORKWUNG, BUT ALSO THAT BY SOME QUIRK OF DESTINY THE HOUSE **NEXT DOOR** TO HIS WAS UP FOR **SALE**.

"AFTER THE LIBRARY WE DEMONSTRATED OUR DEEP HUMANITY BY VISITING THOSE LESS FORTUNATE THAN OURSELVES AT THE 'HOME FOR DISTRESSED WAR VETERANS'.

"THIS IS WHERE OUR MANIAC FRIEND **PULGER** LIVES.

"PULGER DID SOME FIGHTING IN THE **GHOYOGI SLIME JUNGLES,** WHICH SLIGHTLY AFFECTED HIS PERSONALITY.

"I CAN HONESTLY SAY THAT HE IS THE MOST INTERESTING ADULT THAT I HAVE EVER MET.

11

"WE ASKED PULGER IF HE'D LIKE TO BRING SOME OF HIS DIS-TRESSED WAR VETERAN MANIAC FRIENDS FOR A QUIET *HOLIDAY* OUT IN THE SUBURBS.

"PULGER SAID OKAY, AS LONG AS WE COULD ARRANGE A QUAD-ENGINE STRATO-CHOPPER AND THIRTY AIR-TO-GROUND *WARPEDOS* FOR HIS PERSONAL USE.

"I SAID I DIDN'T THINK THAT WOULD BE A PROBLEM.

"NEXT STOP WAS THE CHARITIES' COMMISSION..."

SO LET'S GET THIS *STRAIGHT*, MR DOBBS. YOU WISH TO ESTABLISH YOURSELF AS A *CHARITY* FOR THE REHABILITATION OF, UH...

...OF DANGEROUS MANIAC EX-SERVICEMEN IN NEED OF LOVE AND UNDERSTANDING. YEAH.

WE WILL ALSO NEED A MONSTROUSLY HUGE GOVERNMENT LOAN IN ORDER TO FUND THIS UTTERLY HEART-WRINGING VENTURE.

'SRIGHT.

"THIS CONCLUDED OUR SERVICES TO THE PUBLIC FOR THE MORNING AND WE SPENT AN INNOCENT AFTERNOON OF BOYISH FUN AT THE *LAUGHTERLAND LEISURE LIDO.*

"WITHIN A WEEK THE GOVERN-MENT CHEQUE WAS THROUGH, WHICH QUINCH AND MYSELF PROCEEDED TO SPEND IN A THRIFTY AND THOUGHTFUL MANNER AT THE LOCAL DEPARTMENT STORE—"

...AND WE'LL NEED PLATES, CUPS, CUTLERY, TABLE NAPKINS, BEDCLOTHES, SOAP, A QUAD-ENGINE STRATO-CHOPPER WITH THIRTY AIR-TO-GROUND WARPEDOS, BUTTER, CHEESE, EGGS, BEER...

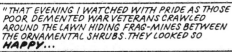

"THAT EVENING I WATCHED WITH PRIDE AS THOSE POOR DEMENTED WAR VETERANS CRAWLED AROUND THE LAWN HIDING FRAG-MINES BETWEEN THE ORNAMENTAL SHRUBS. THEY LOOKED SO **HAPPY**...

"BUT WERE WE DOING **ENOUGH?** WHAT WERE WE DOING TO HELP **INTERWORLD RELATIONSHIPS** AND THE CAUSE OF **GALACTIC PEACE?** NOTHING.

"A MAJOR INITIATIVE WAS CALLED FOR...

HELLO? IS THAT THE **GHOYOGIAN EMBASSY?**

WHO? REVEREND DOBBS OF THE MASSACRE HOUSE UNIVERSAL PEACE AND LOVE INCENTIVE? YOU WANT A GHOYOGIAN PARTY TO VISIT YOUR PLANET? BUT...

WELL, YES, I CAN SEE HOW THAT **WOULD** HELP CEMENT RELATIONS BETWEEN OUR TWO PLANETS AFTER THE STRAIN OF THE **SLIME JUNGLE WARS**...

"WE ARRANGED THE VISIT FOR THE FOLLOWING FNORDSDAY, BUT I DECIDED NOT TO TELL PULGER ABOUT IT JUST YET..."

HOW'RE THINGS, PULGER?

PRETTY GOOD! I'M JUST ARRANGING THESE PUNGEE-SPIKES IN CASE **CHARLIE** TRIES A NIGHT ATTACK! AIN'T HAD THIS MUCH FUN SINCE **GHOYOGI!**

"IT WAS A BALMY SUMMER'S EVENING. NEXT DOOR, JUDGE THORKWUNG AND HIS WIFE HAD GONE TO BED EARLY, SO I SIGNALLED QUINCH TO START THE MORTAR PRACTICE.

"I FELT SORTA WARM INSIDE. I GUESS VIRTUE IS ITS OWN REWARD.

"IN FACT, EVEN HAD I SUSPECTED THEN THE TRULY HORRIFYING SUFFERING AND AMAZING LOSS OF LIFE THAT WOULD BE CAUSED BY OUR WELL-MEANING ENTERPRISE...

"...I'D HAVE DONE IT ANYWAY.

"ONLY **MORE** SO."

THE MAYHEM CONTINUES NEXT PROG!

I WOKE WITH THE TASTE OF CLEAN, SUBURBAN AIR IN MY MOUTH...

Twirrick!

Twirrick!

OUTSIDE, LITTLE BIRDIES WERE TWITTERING DELIGHTFULLY.

BAROOMM

MY NAME IS WALDO "D.R." DOBBS, THE "D.R." STANDING FOR "DIMINISHED RESPONSIBILITY"...

...AND BEING A RESPECTABLE CITIZEN IS THE MOST AMAZINGLY INCREDIBLE FUN I EVER HAD.

IT WAS MIND-ROASTING TO CONSIDER THAT I OWED IT ALL TO JUDGE THORKWUNG...

HE HAD SUGGESTED THAT MY TOTALLY STUPID FRIEND QUINCH AND I DO CHARITY WORK IN ORDER TO SLIGHTLY REDUCE OUR RIDICULOUS JAIL SENTENCES.

THIS HAD PROMPTED US TO ESTABLISH THE CAREFREE HAVEN KNOWN AS 'MASSACRE HOUSE'...

...WHERE UNBALANCED AND LETHAL EX-SERVICEMEN COULD WANDER AROUND WITH WEAPONS SCARING PEOPLE FOR THERAPEUTIC PURPOSES. IT WAS AN IDEALLY-SITUATED RESORT...

...IN FACT, IT WAS RIGHT NEXT DOOR TO THE AFOREMENTIONED JUDGE THORKWUNG.

DOBBS, YOU EVIL, WORTHLESS, TWISTED ANIMAL!

D.R. & QUINCH
GO STRAIGHT!
PART 2

WHEN YOU COME UP FOR TRIAL IN A WEEK OR SO I'M GOING TO *DESTROY* YOU, YOU WARPED LITTLE FIEND! LOOK AT WHAT YOUR *MANIAC* FRIENDS HAVE DONE TO MY *NEIGHBOUR-HOOD!*

2000 A.D.
Credit Card:

SCRIPT ROBOT
Alan Moore

ART ROBOT
Alan Davis

LETTERING ROBOT
Steve Potter

COMPU·73E

HEY, MAN, DID I HEAR YOU REFER TO THESE UNFORTUNATE AND DAMAGED PRODUCTS OF THE INSANITY THAT IS WAR AS *MANIACS?* THAT IS THE MOST TOTALLY UNCHARITABLE ATTITUDE THAT I HAVE EVER *EXPERIENCED*, MAN!

S'RIGHT.

...AND I ONLY HOPE YOU CAN EXPLAIN IT TO THE *MAYOR* AND HIS FELLOW CIVIC DIGNITARIES WHEN THEY ARRIVE THIS AFTERNOON FOR THE OFFICIAL OPENING OF MASSACRE HOUSE.

THE *MAYOR?* HE'S COMING *HERE?*

THIS IS TRUE. HE IS COMING TO PAY HIS RESPECTS TO THESE BRAVE DEFENDERS OF OUR SOIL THAT YOU HAVE CALLOUSLY DUBBED "MANIACS"!

OH, AND BY THE WAY, YOU'RE STANDING IN A RING OF BURIED *FRAG-MINES*, MAN.

I HAD TO CURTAIL THE CONVERSATION AT THIS FASCINATING JUNCTURE, SINCE AS A YOUNG AND DYNAMIC GET-AHEAD CHARITY TYCOON I CANNOT AFFORD TO WASTE TIME IN IDLE CHIT-CHAT.

I HAD THINGS TO DO. LIKE CHECKING THAT THE BLAZOOGAS HAD ARRIVED.

Guns
Beer
Explosives
Lobsters 200000
Grenades

LOOKING BACK I AM DEEPLY ASHAMED THAT IN ALL THIS FLURRY OF ACTIVITY I COMPLETELY FORGOT THAT I HAD ARRANGED A VISIT BY A **GHOYOGIAN DIPLOMATIC PARTY** FOR THE **SAME DAY.**

I SUPPOSE NOBODY'S PERFECT.

ALSO, I SUPPOSE I SHOULD HAVE TOLD PULGER ABOUT THE GHOYOGIAN VISIT IN ADVANCE. PULGER WAS, AFTER ALL, OUR CHIEF DISTRESSED-WAR-VETERAN-IN-RESIDENCE.

TRACTOR PARTS

WITH CARE

PULGER'S ALARMINGLY VOLATILE CONDITION WAS A RESULT OF HIS EXPERIENCES DURING THE RECENTLY-ENDED **GHOYOGI SLIME JUNGLE WARS.**

I AM STILL TOTALLY AMAZED BY THIS STAGGERINGLY UNLUCKY COINCIDENCE.

THE AFTERNOON ARRIVED INCREDIBLY QUICKLY, AND WITH IT, THE MAYOR. THIS EVENT FOUND JUDGE THORKWUNG (WHO HAD SOMEHOW ESCAPED THE FRAG-MINES) IN A STATE OF AGITATION...

MR MAYOR, LET ME **APOLOGISE** FOR ALL THIS...

SKREEE!

QUINCH AND I PRUDENTLY DEPARTED FROM THE SCENE SHORTLY BEFORE THE ARRIVAL OF PULGER'S QUAD-ENGINE STRATOCOPTER (WITH THIRTY AIR-TO-GROUND WARPEDOES.)

THIS IS WHY WE ARE CURRENTLY ALIVE, AS OPPOSED TO OTHERWISE.

BTHWAAM!

ALL THIS HAPPENED TWO WEEKS AGO. WITH THE REMAINDER OF THE CHARITY GRANT WE HAVE SECURED A LUXURY HOTEL ROOM ON THE **COSTA LUNA**.

AS I SIT ON THE VERANDA TYPING THIS, QUINCH IS FILLING THE BATH-TUB WITH **RIPPY FISH**.

ACCORDING TO THE HOLO-NEWS, JUDGE THORKWUNG HAS BEEN CHARGED WITH FULL RESPONSIBILITY FOR THE "**MASSACRE HOUSE MASSACRE**."

ALSO, WE ARE NOW OFFICIALLY AT WAR WITH GHOYOGI AGAIN FOR WARPEDOING THEIR PEACE PARTY.

WE SAID GOODBYE TO PULGER AT THE SPACEPORT YESTERDAY...

ISN'T IT **TERRIFIC?** WE'RE AT WAR WITH **GHOYOGI** AGAIN! ME AN' THE GUYS HAVE ENLISTED FOR AN EIGHT-YEAR TOUR OF DUTY!

LISTEN, I CAN'T THANK YOU KIDS ENOUGH...

HE DIDN'T HAVE TO THANK ME. JUST THE LOOK ON HIS HAPPY, HIDEOUSLY MANGLED FACE WAS ENOUGH TO GIVE ME A WARM GLOW INSIDE.

CHARITABLE DEEDS! THERE'S NOTHING BETTER...

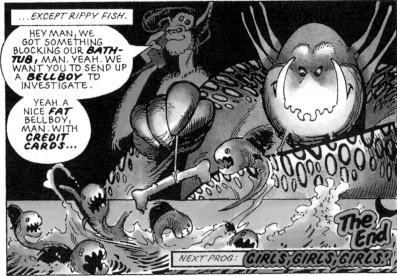

...EXCEPT RIPPY FISH.

HEY MAN, WE GOT SOMETHING BLOCKING OUR **BATH-TUB**, MAN. YEAH. WE WANT YOU TO SEND UP A **BELLBOY** TO INVESTIGATE.

YEAH. A NICE **FAT** BELLBOY, MAN. WITH **CREDIT CARDS**...

The End

NEXT PROG: GIRLS, GIRLS, GIRLS!

"MY NAME IS ERNEST ERROL QUINCH.

"MY MOTHER, WHO IS, LIKE, THIS INCREDIBLY RICH OLD LADY THAT I KNOW, SAYS I'M **EMOTIONALLY DEPRIVED** WITH ACCORDANT BEHAVIOURAL ABERRATIONS.

"THIS MEANS THAT I LIKE STEALING THINGS AND DESTROYING VEHICLES AND TERRORISING PEOPLE WHO HAVE NEVER DONE ME ANY HARM WHATSOEVER.

"THIS IS WHY EVERYBODY **HATES** ME, AND THAT'S WHY I'M EMOTIONALLY DEPRIVED.

"I GOT THIS ONE GUY, LIKE, THAT I KNOW, AND HE'S MY BEST FRIEND. HIS NAME IS WALDO 'D.R.' DOBBS AND HE HAS AN I.Q. OF **280** AND HE BLOWS THINGS UP AND I RESPECT HIM **TOTALLY.**

"ANYWAY, THIS IS A STORY THAT I WROTE WHICH IS INCREDIBLE BECAUSE IT'S GOT US IN IT. IT ALL BEGAN ONE NIGHT WHEN I WENT OVER TO D.R.'S HOUSE TO BORROW HIS FLAME-THROWER...

"...LITTLE KNOWING THAT I WOULD SHORTLY BE PLUNGED INTO THIS TOTALLY HORRIFIC SEQUENCE OF EVENTS THAT I HAVE DECIDED TO CALL..."

2000 A.D.
Credit Card:
SCRIPT ROBOT
ALAN MOORE
ART ROBOT
ALAN DAVIS
LETTERING ROBOT
STEVE POTTER
COMPU·73ᴇ

D.R. & QUINCH
GO GIRL CRAZY!
PART 1

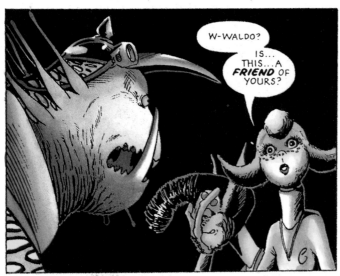

W-WALDO? IS...THIS...A **FRIEND** OF YOURS?

UH...

UH, YEAH. THIS IS MY FRIEND **ERNEST.**

ERNEST, I'D, UH, LIKE YOU TO MEET **CHRYSOPRASIA...**

UH, CHRYSOPRASIA, MAYBE WE COULD HAVE A WORD IN **PRIVATE...**

SIT DOWN ERNEST, OLD BUDDY. GET YOURSELF A DRINK...

UH, LISTEN, ERNEST IS... UH...

WELL, HE'S THIS KID IN THE **SLOW READING GROUP** UP AT COLLEGE, KNOW WHAT I MEAN?

I FELT **SORRY** FOR HIM. HE'S UNBELIEVABLY STUPID AND... AND I, UH, VOLUNTEERED TO **HELP HIM** WITH HIS STUDIES AFTER SCHOOL AND, UH...

LOOK, I'M FANTASTICALLY SORRY ABOUT THIS...

SORRY?

BUT WALDO, I THINK THAT'S JUST **WONDERFUL!**

LET'S GO AND **TALK** TO THE POOR CREATURE.

WELL, ERNEST, I'VE BEEN HEARING A LOT ABOUT YOU. HOW LONG HAVE YOU *KNOWN* MY WALDO?

HUH? *D.R.*?

D.R.? WHO'S...

OH, THAT'S A SORT OF SILLY NICKNAME. IT'S SHORT FOR *'DEEPLY RELIGIOUS'.*

LISTEN, I JUST REMEMBERED I WAS PLANNING ON US GOING OUT TONIGHT...

OH, THAT'LL BE *FUN!* WE CAN GO DOWN TO THE YOUTH CLUB! THAT WAY, ERNEST CAN COME TOO! DO YOU DANCE THE *FROGGY-HOP*, ERNEST?

"SO ANYWAY, WE DROVE DOWN TO THIS UTTER DIRTBALL OF A YOUTH CLUB..."

YOU KNOW, *I* USED TO HAVE A NICKNAME, TOO! YOU'LL NEVER GUESS...

THEY USED TO CALL ME *'CHIRPY'.* ISN'T THAT *SILLY?*

"I HADN'T BEEN DOWN THERE FOR A WHILE, BUT PEOPLE STILL REMEMBERED ME..."

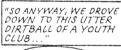
AAAAAAAEEEEGH!

LET ME *OUT!* I'VE GOT A RARE *BLOOD GROUP!*

LOOK... HERE'S ALL OF OUR MONEY! PLEASE, TAKE IT!

IT'S A SORT OF CHARITABLE SCHEME THAT I INSTITUTED...

IT'S TO HELP ERNEST PAY FOR THIS ASTOUNDINGLY COMPLICATED *BRAIN OPERATION* THAT HE NEEDS...

23

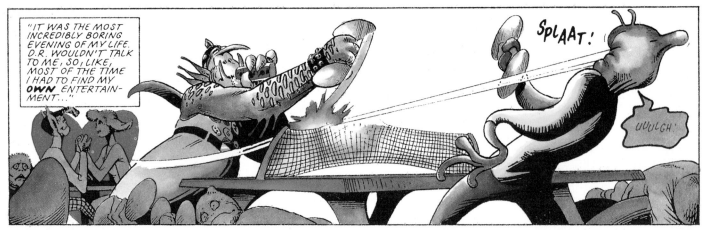

"IT WAS THE MOST INCREDIBLY BORING EVENING OF MY LIFE. D.R. WOULDN'T TALK TO ME, SO, LIKE, MOST OF THE TIME I HAD TO FIND MY *OWN* ENTERTAINMENT..."

SPLAAT!

UUULGH.

"PRETTY SOON, WE HAD TO GO HOME. THIS WAS BASICALLY BECAUSE 'CHIRPY' HAS TO BE IN BY NINE O'CLOCK, WHICH IS, LIKE, TOTALLY DISGUSTING IN MY OPINION..."

"EVENTUALLY, WE WERE ALONE..."

UH, LOOK I SUPPOSE YOU'RE WONDERING ABOUT CHRYSOPRASIA...

S'RIGHT.

SHE'S THE NEW *DRAMA COACH'S* DAUGHTER. I BUMPED INTO HER ON CAMPUS ONE DAY, AND... WELL, EVER SINCE THEN I JUST CAN'T STOP THINKING ABOUT HER.

I TRIED TO CONCENTRATE ON SOMETHING WORTHWHILE LIKE FORGING BANK NOTES AND MAKING A SHRINK GUN. STUFF LIKE THAT...

IT DIDN'T WORK. EVERYTIME I PICKED UP AN IMPLODER CAP I SAW HER FACE.

I...

I THINK I'M IN LOVE.

25

WHAT ARE
YOU..?

OH! IT'S *YOU!*
WALDO'S FRIEND
ERNEST, FROM THE
'SLOW READER'
GROUP!

ERNEST, TAKE
ME DOWN IMMEDIATELY.
I KNOW THIS IS JUST
YOUR IDEA OF A BOYISH
PRANK, BUT...

BUT...
ERNEST...WHAT
YOU'RE POINTING AT ME
IS A VERY DANGEROUS
WEAPON THAT COULD GO
OFF AND HURT
SOMEBODY.

S'RIGHT.

"SHE WAS UNBELIEVABLY QUIET FOR THE REST OF THE
JOURNEY APART FROM THE WEIRD, SQUEAKY LITTLE 'EE-OUK'
NOISE THAT SHE KEPT MAKING IN HER THROAT."

"I TOOK HER OVER TO OUR SECRET HIDEOUT
ON THE INTERSECTION OF STRANGLER'S
ROW AND 672nd. STREET. SHE STILL
DIDN'T SAY ANYTHING EXCEPT 'EE-OUK'."

"I GUESS SHE WAS JUST
TOTALLY AWESTRUCK."

"WHEN SHE SAW WHAT
I HAD PLANNED FOR
HER SHE PLEADED
PATHETICALLY..."

EE-OUK.

HOME MOVIES?
ERNEST, THAT'S VERY
SWEET, BUT TONIGHT IS
THE OPENING OF THE *PLAY*
THAT WALDO AND I ARE
APPEARING IN...

"THIS INCREDIBLY
STUPID PLAY, WHICH
STARRED THE BRAIN-
WASHED DOBBS,
WAS CALLED 'THE
BLEATING HEART'.
I COULD NOT STAND
BY AND SEE MY
PAL HUMILIATED
IN THIS FASHION.

"MERCILESSLY, I STARTED
THE PROJECTOR..."

"SO AS NOT TO UNHINGE HER IMMEDIATELY, I STARTED OUT WITH A MILD TRAVELOGUE DESCRIBING THE ASTONISHINGLY FANTASTIC TIME WE HAD ON OUR SUMMER VACATION."

"AFTER THAT I SHOWED HER VIVID PICTORIAL EVIDENCE OF THE WAY IN WHICH DOBBS HAD GREATLY IMPROVED THE ANNUAL FIREWORKS DISPLAY OF THE LADY SKROAT-FANCIER'S GUILD..."

"I FOLLOWED THIS WITH EXCERPTS FROM DOBBS' FORTHCOMING DOCUMENTARY CONCERNING HIS INCREDIBLE LIFE, ENTITLED 'MY INCREDIBLE LIFE. BY WALDO (D.R.) DOBBS'."

"I COULD TELL THAT SHE WAS IMPRESSED BY THE CAMERA-WORK DURING THE SCENE WITH THE BABY NEWTS AND THE GIANT PENCIL-SHARPENER."

EE-OUK!

"OUT OF BASIC HUMAN SYMPATHY I CALLED AN INTERMISSION AND SERVED REFRESHMENTS."

"ASTOUNDINGLY, IT TURNED OUT THAT SHE DIDN'T HAVE ANY MONEY..."

"...SO I MADE HER WATCH 'MIDNIGHT MADNESS AT THE MORGUE WITH D.R. AND QUINCH', WHICH IS THIS SERIOUS ART FILM THAT WE MADE FOR THE CENTRAVIAN FILM FESTIVAL."

GHEEYAAAAAAGH!

"FINALLY, THE ROSEATE VEIL OF LOVE'S DELUSIONS WAS WAFTED FROM OFF HER LIMPID EYES, AND SHE REALISED WHAT AN UTTERLY FILTHY, INSANE, DIRTBALL THIS DOBBS GUY WAS.

"I UNTIED HER. SHE'D SUFFERED ENOUGH."

"IN FACT, SHE MAY EVEN HAVE SUFFERED A LITTLE *TOO* MUCH, MARBLES-WISE..."

OH, I'M SO ASHAMED!

TO THINK THAT ALL THIS TIME, MY WALDO HAS ACTUALLY BEEN A VILE AND UNSPEAKABLE HOMICIDAL THUG!

WHAT A GOODY TWO-FLIPPERS HE MUST HAVE THOUGHT ME!

OH, ERNEST... I SEE NOW THAT I'VE BEEN *UNWORTHY* OF HIM!

I'LL *TRY* TO CHANGE MY WAYS, I PROMISE...

NO MORE MISS PRIM-AND-PROPER FOR ME! *OH* NO!

NO MORE STAYING BEHIND TO STACK THE CHAIRS UP AFTER NEEDLE CLASS!

NO MORE CLEANING MY TEETH AND FREESTYLE SQUARE-DANCING!

FROM NOW ON, I'M GOING TO BE THE KIND OF WOMAN THAT MY WALDO *DESERVES!*

IT'S GOODBYE *CHRYSO-PRASIA* AND HELLO *CRAZY CHRYSSIE!*

GIMME THAT *BEER*, PIG-BREATH!

"TO BE ABSOLUTELY HONEST, I FOUND THE SITUATION AMAZINGLY UNUSUAL."

OKAY, HUNK... *DRIVE!*

"OUR FIRST STOP WAS A REPUTED FASHION HOUSE WHERE THE NOW TOTALLY MUTATED CHRYSOPRASIA ENQUIRED AFTER THE CURRENT TRENDS IN LADIES' WEAR."

GIMME TWO OF EVERYTHING YA GOT, DIRTBAG!

"NEXT, A NEIGHBOURHOOD DRINKS STORE..."

LOAD HER UP, SCUMBALL. OH YEAH... AND HAVE ONE YOURSELF WHILE YOU'RE AT IT...

"...A TATTOO PARLOUR..."

A BURNING CROCODILE BEING ATTACKED BY A PUTREFYING ZOMBIE CARRYING A CHAINSAW... AND MAKE IT *SNAPPY!*

"UNTIL FINALLY..."

⟨URP!⟩

Y'KNOW QUINCH, YOU BRAINLESS MUDBAG, THIS IS THE MOST AMAZINGLY INCREDIBLE FUN I EVER HAD!

ME AND D.R. ARE MORE SUITED TO EACH OTHER THAN *EVER!* LET'S DRIVE OVER TO THE THEATRE WHERE 'THE BLEATING HEART' IS OPENING AND SHOW HIM THE *NEW ME!*

"WHAT COULD I DO?"

"I HAD CREATED A DEMENTED SLAVERING MONSTER WHEN I ONLY WISHED TO HELP AN INNOCENT LITTLE GIRL.

"IN MY EXPERIENCE, THIS IS WHAT HAPPENS WHEN YOU TRY TO BE A NICE GUY."

EE-OUK!

NEXT PROG: **A NIGHT AT THE THEATRE!**

"MY NAME IS **ERNEST ERROL QUINCH**, COLLEGE STUDENT AND PHILOSOPHER."

"I OFTEN HAVE THESE, LIKE, TOTALLY INCREDIBLE **THOUGHTS** THAT ARE, LIKE, **INSIDE** MY HEAD..."

"I ASK MYSELF AMAZINGLY DEEP QUESTIONS OF A MORAL NATURE..."

"LIKE, WAS IT RIGHT TO REVEAL THE SICKENING TRUTH ABOUT MY EX-COLLEAGUE **WALDO 'D.R.' DOBBS** TO HIS PATHETIC, SIMPERING GIRL-FRIEND?"

"AND— SHOULDN'T I BE **ASHAMED** TO THINK THIS KNOWLEDGE HAD COMPLETELY PULVERISED HER FEEBLE MIND AND ALTERED HER PERSONALITY TO THAT OF A SLAVERING FIEND FROM THE PIT?"

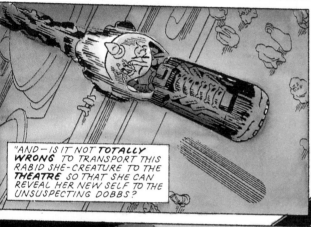

"AND— IS IT NOT **TOTALLY WRONG** TO TRANSPORT THIS RABID SHE-CREATURE TO THE **THEATRE** SO THAT SHE CAN REVEAL HER NEW SELF TO THE UNSUSPECTING DOBBS?"

"AND FINALLY, AM I PREPARED TO TAKE RESPONSIBILITY FOR THE WAY IN WHICH MY ACTIONS HAVE COMPLETELY RUINED AN INNOCENT YOUNG LIFE?"

"THE ANSWER TO ALL THESE QUESTIONS IS AN AMAZINGLY SIMPLE ONE:

"NO."

2000 A.D. **Credit Card:**

SCRIPT ROBOT
ALAN MOORE

ART ROBOT
ALAN DAVIS

LETTERING ROBOT
STEVE POTTER

COMPU-73

D.R. & QUINCH
GO GIRL CRAZY!
PART 3

"I ONLY HOPED THAT D.R. WOULD SEE THESE THINGS IN THE SAME CLEAR, PHILOSOPHICAL LIGHT AS I DID..."

LOOK, WALDO... I KNOW THIS IS *UPSETTING* FOR AN *ARTISTE* OF YOUR *SENSITIVITY,* BUT THERE'S NOTHING ELSE FOR IT...

...THE SHOW MUST GO ON, EVEN IF *CHRYSOPRASIA* ISN'T *HERE* YET!

HEY, MAN! I HAVE, LIKE, TOTAL FAITH IN HER. FOR THIS REASON I WILL DO THESE UNARTISTIC-TYPE THINGS THAT YOU ARE ASKING OF ME.

GOOD MAN! I'M SURE MY DAUGHTER WILL ARRIVE IN TIME FOR HER ENTRANCE.

NOW, GET OUT THERE AND GIVE 'EM ALL YOU'VE GOT!

UH, "AHEM", MAN...

BUT, LIKE, SOFT, MAN... WHAT'S ALL THIS LIGHT THAT THROUGH YONDER WINDOW BREAKS?

A HORSE! A HORSE! SOMEBODY GIVE ME A HORSE, MAN, BECAUSE I COME TO BURY THIS DIRTBALL, NOT TO PRAISE HIM. WHADDYA THINK I AM?

WHETHER IT'S NOBLER FOR THE MIND TO MAKE PEOPLE SUFFER WITH ALL THESE TOTALLY OUTRAGEOUS ARROWS FOR A FORTUNE, OR WHAT!

33

OKAY, THAT SOUNDS GOOD ENOUGH TO ME! GET HER INTO THE *ANTI-THRASH JACKET*, MEN...

W-*WALDO?*

I CANNOT TELL A LIE, MAN. IT WAS *HER!*

WALDO! I DID IT *ALL* FOR *YOU!* ♫ *SOB.* ♫ SAY YOU'LL *WAIT* FOR ME!

FIFTY YEARS ISN'T TOO LONG TO WAIT, IS IT WALDO? WALDO?

HOW COULD I HAVE EVER FELT THE REMOTEST SHRED OF AFFECTION FOR SUCH A HIDEOUS CREATURE, MAN? UNLESS...

...UNLESS I HAD BEEN DRIVEN *TEMPORARILY INSANE* BY SECRET *TRACE CHEMICALS* HIDDEN WITHIN THAT *VEGAN TAKEAWAY MEAL* THAT I ATE A MONTH AGO!

I MUST HAVE *INSTANT REVENGE* UPON THESE MURDEROUS ALIEN RESTAURATEURS! BUT *HOW?*

A *THORIUM BOMB?* OF MY VERY OWN?

Y'KNOW... A KISS ON THE HAND *MAY* BE QUITE CONTINENTAL, MAN...

...BUT TACTICAL THERMONUCLEAR WEAPONRY IS A GUY'S BEST FRIEND!

S'RIGHT.

The End

NEXT PROG: *YOU'RE IN THE ARMY NOW!*

"I WOKE UP IN THE EAZE-CLEAN.

"I HAVE NO IDEA HOW I CAME TO BE IN THIS INCREDIBLY STRANGE, CONFUSING SITUATION.

"ACTUALLY, IT HAS NOTHING TO DO WITH THE FOLLOWING TOTALLY AWESOME STORY AND I'D ADVISE YOU TO FORGET IT, MAN.

"I DECIDED TO VISIT THE ZOOLOGICAL GARDENS NEXT DOOR AND LASER-GRILL MYSELF SOME BREAKFAST.

"CROSSING THE KITCHEN, I WAS FANTASTICALLY ASTONISHED TO DISCOVER A DEAD HYPER-WHALE.

"LOOKING CLOSER I WAS RELIEVED TO DISCOVER THAT IT WAS MY GREAT, SINCERE, AND ONLY MODERATELY BRAIN-DEAD COLLEAGUE ERNEST ERROL QUINCH.

"I LET HIM SLEEP. HE LOOKED SO HAPPY, MAN.

"ON MY WAY OUT TO THE DOOR I NOTICED THIS AMAZINGLY ORDINARY ENVELOPE, WHICH WAS, LIKE, ON MY DOORMAT.

"I PICKED IT UP AND TOOK A LOOK.

"AS IT TURNED OUT, THIS WAS THE MOST ABOMINABLY TERRIBLE MISTAKE THAT I HAVE EVER MADE IN MY ENTIRE LIFE, MAN."

MINISTRY OF WAR

Mr. E.E. Quinch &
Mr. W.D.R. Dobbs,
8 Gotterdammerung Crescent

INDUCTION NOTICE

2000 A.D.
Credit Card:
SCRIPT ROBOT
ALAN MOORE
ART ROBOT
ALAN DAVIS
LETTERING ROBOT
STEVE POTTER
COMPU·73ₑ

D.R. & QUINCH
GET DRAFTED
PART 1

"SGT. RORCHMUTT REPLIED WITH SOME VERY INTERESTING OPINIONS, MANY OF THEM ABOUT *ME*.

"I WAS TOTALLY SHOCKED BY HIS DEEP PREJUDICE AGAINST FUN-LOVING COLLEGE STUDENTS AND DECIDED THAT HE MUST BE DESTROYED AS SOON AS POSSIBLE.

"UNFORTUNATELY, OUR ENTIRE PLATOON WAS *POSTED* THE NEXT DAY. THE DEPARTURE WAS A STIRRING AFFAIR WITH LOTS OF SINGING..."

WE'RE SPACE MARINES! WE'RE GLORIOUS
WE'RE STEADFAST, BRAVE AND TRUE!
SO DON'T YOU DIRTBAGS MESS WITH US,
OR THIS IS WHAT WE'LL DO :

WE'LL NICK YOUR DOGS,
WE'LL NUKE YOUR SCHOOLS!
WE'LL STRETCH YOU ON A RACK!
WE'LL BORROW ALL YOUR GARDEN TOOLS
AND NEVER GIVE THEM BACK!

"THERE WERE FORTY-SIX VERSES OF THIS TREMENDOUSLY CATCHY NUMBER.

"ONCE WE WERE IN DEEP SPACE, SGT. RORCHMUTT TOLD US WHERE WE WERE ACTUALLY GOING..."

KNOW *WHAT?* YOU *WHIMPERING, WHINING, WHEEDLING WADS* OF *WORMBAIT* ARE GOING TO...

GHOYOGIA!!

GHOYOGIA? WHERE THE SALIVA-TREES DIGEST YOU ALIVE?

GHOYOGIA, WHERE EVEN THE TERRIBLE DISEASES HAVE TERRIBLE DISEASES??

HEY MAN, WHAT KIND OF *EXPENSIVE FOREIGN RESTAURANTS* DO THEY HAVE IN THIS PLACE?

THERE *ARE* NO EXPENSIVE FOREIGN RESTAURANTS ON GHOYOGIA!

AAWAUUGHH!

"IT WAS, LIKE, MY FIRST EXPOSURE TO THE TOTAL INSANITY THAT IS WAR. AND THERE WAS WORSE TO COME, MAN..."

NEXT. PROG. *APOCALYPSE SHORTLY!*

"I TUCKED THE LETTER AWAY AND RESUMED MY WATCHFUL VIGILANCE, WHICH IS, LIKE, UTTERLY VITAL WHEN YOU'RE ON **JUNGLE PATROL.**

"SOMEWHERE IN THIS DISGUSTING, RANCID UNDERGROWTH LURKED **THE ENEMY...**"

HEY MAN, I THINK I HAVE LOCATED THE ENEMY CAMP WITH MY ASTONISHINGLY AWESOME TRACKING SKILLS. THIS CALLS FOR SOME DELICATE, CAREFULLY-CONSTRUCTED STRATEGY.

FASS ME UP THE **BAZOOKER-NUKER,** MAN...

"ADJUSTING MY EARMUFFS AND FLASHGOGGLES, I GAVE THE **OFFICIAL SPACE MARINES WAR-CRY...**"

FAZZOOM!

"WHO CAN SAY WHAT THOUGHTS WERE UPPERMOST IN MY STAGGERINGLY BRILLIANT MIND AT THAT MOMENT, MAN?

EAT PLUTONIUM DEATH, YOU DISGUSTING ALIEN WEIRDOS!

"I HOPED THERE WOULD BE PRISONERS, AS I HAD INVENTED A TOTALLY NEW CONCEPT IN TORTURE DURING BREAKFAST..."

43

TAKE THESE EVIL, REPULSIVE LITTLE MAGGOTS AND LOCK THEM UP!

PUT THEM IN *CUBICLE FIFTEEN* WITH THE *MAN-MONSTER!*

BOY, ARE *YOU* GUYS FOR IT! I FEEL SORRY FOR YA!

MAN-MONSTER?

YEAH... I KNOW YOU JUST FIRED A THERMO-NUCLEAR WARHEAD AT US, BUT I WOULDN'T WISH THE *MAN-MONSTER* ON *ANYBODY!*

YEAH. HE'S THIS GUY WHO'S BEEN TURNED INTO A PSYCHOTIC KILLING MACHINE BY THE HORRORS OF WAR.

THEY SAY HE *EATS* PEOPLE WHO GET LOCKED UP WITH HIM.

ANY LAST REQUESTS, YOU GUYS?

"I GAVE HIM MY LETTER TO MRS QUINCH AND THEN THEY LOCKED THE DOOR BEHIND US.

"IN THE FAR CORNER, SOMETHING GROWLED. MY SPINE WAS, LIKE, TOTALLY CHILLED, MAN.

"SOMETHING BEGAN TO SHUFFLE TOWARDS US. I COULD SEE ITS FACE... ITS CRAZED EYES WERE GLEAMING. FOAM DRIPPED FROM ITS SLAVERING JAWS.

"I FELT I HAD TO *SAY* SOMETHING..."

HOW'S IT GOIN', PULGER?

NEXT PROG: THE FANTASTIC INCREDIBLY GREAT ESCAPE!

IT'S AN OLD TRICK, BUT IT MIGHT JUST WORK!

PULGER, WHY DON'T WE JUST, LIKE, USE THE ESCAPE TUNNEL *OURSELVES*, MAN?

HMMM.. I DUNNO... THERE'S SO MUCH THAT COULD GO *WRONG*... AHH, WHAT THE HECK! I LIKE YOUR STYLE, KID! LET'S GIVE IT THE OLD COLLEGE TRY...

"WHICH IS, LIKE, EXACTLY WHAT WE DID...

"TO THIS DAY, I AM UNABLE TO UNDERSTAND HOW SUCH A TOTALLY INGENIOUS PLAN COULD GO SO AMAZINGLY, HORRIBLY WRONG...

"IT ALL STARTED OUT SO *PROMISINGLY*..."

HEY MAN, I GOTTA HAND IT TO YOU. FOR A DISTRESSED MANIAC WAR VETERAN, YOU DIG A TOTALLY AWESOME TUNNEL.

I DIDN'T BUILD ALL *THIS*. WHAT DO YOU THINK I *AM*? *INSANE* OR SOMETHING?

I JUST *DISCOVERED* IT. IT'S PART OF A WARREN BUILT BY TINY GHOYOGIAN *BURROWING ANIMALS* CALLED 'SNUFFLEGRUFFS'.

HMMM...
HEY, MAN...
WHY DO THESE
TINY, CUDDLY AND
LOVABLE-SOUNDING
ANIMALS BUILD
SUCH FANTASTICALLY
COLOSSAL
TUNNELS?

HMMM.
I DUNNO.
PERHAPS THEY'RE
CLAUSTROPHOBIC...

SNUFFLE
SNUFFLE
SNUFFLE

GGRRRRRRUFF!

IT'S OKAY,
BOYS! I CAME
PREPARED FOR
A **SNEAK
ATTACK!**
DON'T
COME ANY
CLOSER, OR
I FIRE!

PULGER!
THAT GUN IS
MADE OUT OF
SOAP, MAN!

YEAH...
BUT **HE**
DOESN'T
KNOW
THAT!

GGRRRRRUFF!

"AFTER THAT, EVENTS BECAME INCREDIBLY UNUSUAL..."

"AS A FAMOUS POET ONCE SAID 'DISCRETION IS, LIKE, THE BETTER PART OF VALOUR, LIKE, TOTALLY.'"

"INCIDENTALLY, IT WAS NOT ME WHO SAID THIS AMAZINGLY TRUE STUFF, BUT ANOTHER FAMOUS POET."

RUN FOR IT, BOYS! YOU'RE YOUNG WITH YOUR LIVES STILL AHEAD OF YOU! I'LL HOLD HIM OFF AS LONG AS I CAN!

"EVENTUALLY..."

HEY, MAN, WHAT IS THIS STONE SLAB THAT I PERCEIVE WITH MY EYES, MAN?

IT MUST BE THE OTHER END OF PULGER'S TUNNEL!

S'RIGHT.

?

?

HEY, YOU DIRTBAG! WHAT ARE YOU DOING IN MY ESCAPE TUNNEL?

YOU'RE NOT EVEN A GHOYOGIAN! WHAT DO YOU MEAN USING MY TUNNEL OUT OF THE GHOYOGIAN PENAL STOCKADE?

C-Chrysoprasia?

Waldo?

All soldiers leave a girl
                behind
That worships and
                adores 'em
But mine's here on
        Ghoyogi, too,
Which is, like,
        unbelievably awesome.
    P.F.C. Waldo Dobbs
    (His second sonnet)

NEXT PROG: THE SNUFFLEGRUFFS OF WAR!

49

"*OLDSTERS, WHO ARE, LIKE, TOTAL VACUUM-HEADS AND DO NOT UNDERSTAND THE PROBLEMS OF A YOUNG PERSON OF TODAY, OFTEN GET THE WRONG IDEA ABOUT WALDO 'D.R.' DOBBS, WHO IS LIKE ME, MAN.*"

"*THEY THINK THAT I HAVE NO ROMANCE IN MY SOUL, WHICH IS, LIKE, THIS INCREDIBLY STRANGE THING THAT I HAVE INSIDE MY BODY.*"

"*TO THEM I SAY: 'YOU ARE TOTALLY INCORRECT, MAN.'*"

"*WHY, WHEN I SAW CHRYSOPRASIA STANDING THERE IN THAT GHOYOGIAN PENAL STOCKADE, I WAS, LIKE, TOTALLY OVERCOME WITH ROMANTIC EMOTIONS. SHE WAS JUST AS I REMEMBERED HER...*"

D.R. & QUINCH
GET DRAFTED
PART 4

"*IN FACT, I WAS SO INCREDIBLY ROMANCED-OUT THAT I THOUGHT MY HEART WAS GOING TO STOP, MAN.*"

ARK!

WORM!

MAGGOT!!

SCUMPOT!!!

2000 A.D.
Credit Card:
SCRIPT ROBOT
ALAN MOORE
ART ROBOT
ALAN DAVIS
LETTERING ROBOT
STEVE POTTER
COMPU·73E

CHRYSOPRASIA, MAN, I ASK YOU TO STOP THIS SENSELESS VIOLENCE THAT YOU ARE, LIKE, DOING TO ME.

WHAT ARE YOU DOING IN MY CELL, YOU TREACHEROUS LITTLE GREASE-BALL?

"*CHRYSOPRASIA STILL HAD STRONG FEELINGS FOR ME, TOO.*"

HEY, MAN, IT WAS AN AMAZINGLY UNFORTUNATE ACCIDENT THAT COULD HAVE HAPPENED TO ANYBODY...

S'RIGHT.

WE WERE ESCAPING FROM A *CENTRAVIAN PENAL STOCKADE* THROUGH THESE ASTONISHING TUNNELS MADE BY UTTERLY HORRIBLE *MOLE-MONSTERS*, AND...

...AND CAME UP IN A *GHOYOGIAN PENAL STOCKADE!* HA! IT SERVES YOU *RIGHT*, YOU MALICIOUS BLOB OF *FILTH!*

I AM, LIKE, TOTALLY DEPRESSED.

YOU'RE DEPRESSED?? WHAT ABOUT *ME??* YOU RUINED MY LIFE, YOU DEGENERATE *REPTILE!*

AFTER I ESCAPED FROM THAT *INSTITUTION* THAT DADDY PUT ME IN, I HAD TO BECOME A *MERCENARY* FOR THE *GHOYOGIANS* IN ORDER TO *SURVIVE!*

I PLAY ONE LITTLE PRACTICAL JOKE WITH SOME FRAG-MINES AND THEY SLING ME INTO THIS FILTH-BAG *PENAL STOCKADE!* YOU'VE *DESTROYED MY LIFE,* WALDO!

HEY, MAN, CAN'T YOU TAKE A JOKE, OR WHAT?

A *JOKE??* YOU WORTHLESS, DISEASED *MOLLUSC!* YOU WON'T *BELIEVE* WHAT'S GOING TO HAPPEN TO YOU NEXT!!

"THIS WAS UNBELIEVABLY TRUE."

ALL RIGHT! NOBODY MOVE!! UP AGAINST THE WALL!

HEY, PULGER, MAN... IT'S, LIKE, US!

BOYS! I THOUGHT YOU WERE *DEAD!* I THOUGHT YOU'D BECOME VICTIMS OF THIS *WAR*...

...THIS DAMNED, *DIRTY* LITTLE WAR.

UH, THIS IS *PULGER*. HE'S THIS DISTRESSED WAR VETERAN THAT WE KNOW. HE HELPED US *ESCAPE* INTO HERE!

THANKS, BOYS. I'M TOUCHED.

BUT HOW DID YOU GET AWAY FROM THE SNUFFLEGRUFF, PULGER? I TAKE IT THAT YOU SHOOK OFF THAT DISTURBINGLY HUGE AND REPULSIVE MONSTER THAT WAS TRYING TO, LIKE, EAT YOU, DOWN IN THE TUNNELS?

WELL, NO...

SNUFFLE SNUFFLE SNUFFLE

...NOT EXACTLY.

GGGRRRRRUUUFFF!!!

"MEANWHILE, LIKE, OUTSIDE...!!"

SHURRUNCH

"IN ONE MIGHTY BOUND, WE WERE, LIKE, TOTALLY FREE."

A'EEE!

IT IS THE **FOREIGN DEVILS** WHO HAVE DONE US THIS DIS-HONOUR!

THE **DEATH OF A THOUSAND PRODS IN THE NAVEL** SHALL BE THEIRS!

AFTER THEM!

"WE ESCAPED INTO THE SLIME JUNGLES, WHICH ARE CALLED 'SLIME JUNGLES' BECAUSE THEY ARE THESE **JUNGLES** THAT ARE, LIKE, TOTALLY COVERED IN **SLIME**."

EW! GROSS!

COME ON, BOYS! GIVE ME **LIBERTY**, OR GIVE ME...

death?

HEY MAN, I DUNNO ABOUT THIS **DEATH** BUSINESS. JUST GIVE ME **LIBERTY**, MAN. I'LL BE OKAY.

SILENCE, YOU TREASONOUS **VERMIN!**

54

"**I** CANNOT BEGIN TO DESCRIBE THE SERIOUSNESS OF OUR SITUATION, MAN.

"THERE WE WERE — TWO AVERAGE, LIKEABLE COLLEGE STUDENTS, A DRAMA COACH'S DAUGHTER TURNED MERCENARY, AND A DISTRESSED WAR VETERAN WEARING A DRESS.

"ON **ONE** SIDE, THERE WERE ALL THESE AMAZINGLY HOSTILE ALIEN SOLDIERS WHO WERE, LIKE, CHARGING AT US AND SHOUTING **UNBELIEVABLY** RUDE AND THREATENING REMARKS...

"...AND ON THE OTHER SIDE THERE WAS **ANOTHER** BUNCH OF AMAZINGLY HOSTILE ALIEN SOLDIERS WHO WERE, LIKE, DOING **EXACTLY THE SAME THING**, MAN! TALK ABOUT **COINCI-DENCE!**

"THEN THE SPIRIT MOVED WITHIN ME, FORCING ME TO, LIKE, CRY OUT AT THE HORROR AND INJUSTICE OF WAR...

HEY, MAN!

D.R. & QUINCH
GET DRAFTED!
PART 5

WHY CAN'T EVERYBODY JUST, Y'KNOW, BE **FRIENDS** AND **EVERYTHING?**

2000 A.D.
Credit Card:
SCRIPT ROBOT
ALAN MOORE
ART ROBOT
ALAN DAVIS
LETTERING ROBOT
STEVE POTTER
COMPU-73E

uh...
and, um...
er...

and,
uh...

...AND *LOVE* EACH OTHER! I HAVE JUST, LIKE, HAD THIS INCREDIBLE *VISION*, MAN, ABOUT HOW WE SHOULD ALL *LOVE* EACH OTHER AND BE *TOTALLY FRIENDLY*...

LIKE, I SAW THIS COMPLETELY AWESOME *LIGHT* THAT WAS, LIKE, *SHINING*, Y'KNOW, INTO MY *EYES*, MAN. AND I HEARD THIS FANTASTICALLY IMPRESSIVE *BARITONE VOICE*...

IT SAID— "WALDO?"

I SAID— "YEAH? WHAT?"

IT SAID—"WALDO, CAN YOU HEAR ME?"

I SAID—"YEAH, MAN, I CAN HEAR YOU WITH, LIKE, ASTOUNDING CLARITY."

SO THEN IT SAID—"I JUST WANT YOU TO KNOW THAT WE SHOULD ALL *LOVE* EACH OTHER, AND BE TOTALLY *FRIENDLY*...

"...AND I WANT YOU TO TELL EVERYBODY THIS, AND, LIKE, IF ANYBODY GETS *SMART* WITH YOU, I WILL DO SOMETHING *INCREDIBLY STRANGE* TO THEM AND THEIR *BRAINS* WILL EXPLODE."

SO, LIKE, I SAID—"OH YEAH?"...

HEY, KID...

YOU WERE DOING OKAY UNTIL THE BIT ABOUT THE *BARITONE.*

HOPE YOU DON'T MIND A LITTLE CRITICISM FROM AN OLD WARHORSE WHO SHOOTS FROM THE HIP...

Hey man, feel free.

"THE SOLDIERS SLID BACK THE BOLTS ON THEIR MOLECULAR-DISPLACEMENT MUSKETS.

56

"IT WAS UNBELIEVABLY DISGUSTING, MAN. IT WAS THE SINGLE MOST DISGUSTING OBJECT I HAVE EVER SEEN EXCEPT WHEN QUINCH WAS CHEWING A *BLISTER-WHELK* ONCE AND OPENED HIS MOUTH TO SHOW EVERYBODY..."

"IT ROLLED FORWARDS, TOTALLY SQUASHING ALL OF THE SOLDIERS, WHICH WAS, LIKE, A MAJOR SETBACK TO THEIR OVERALL STRATEGY.

SQUELCH!

"ON AND ON IT CAME. ON AND ON AND ON AND ON AND ON, MAN..."

OH, GROSS *OUT!*

"ITS HUGE, BLUBBERY LIPS SQUELCHED OPEN. A TERRIBLY HORRIBLE SOUND ROLLED UP FROM THE DEPTHS OF ITS QUIVERING MASS..."

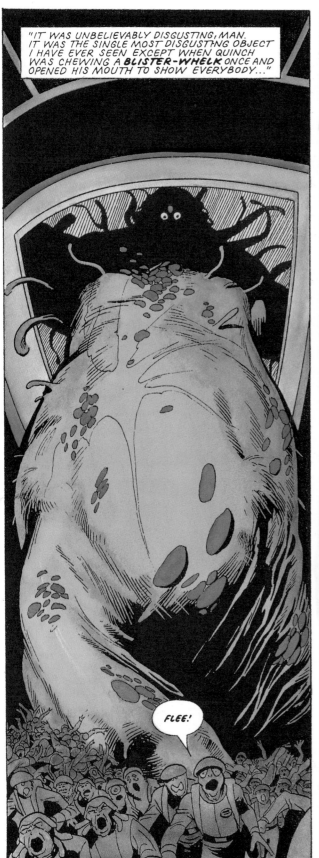

FLEE!

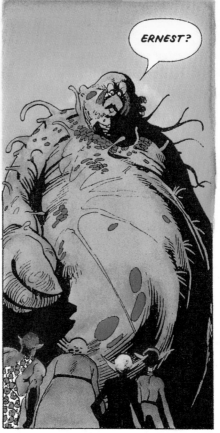

ERNEST?

OH, HI, MOM.

I CAME AS *SOON* AS I GOT LITTLE WALDO'S *LETTER* ASKING TO BE RESCUED. HOW'S MUMMY'S *DUMMY-DUMPLINGS?*

SQUUU-UCK!

WELL, WHATEVER ARE WE ALL DOING STANDING ABOUT IN THIS DREADFUL STICKY JUNGLE WITH ALL THESE *DEAD* PEOPLE?

LET'S GO INSIDE MY COSY INTER-COSMIC MEGA-PALACE, AND HAVE A NICE CUP OF TEA AND A *SCONE.*

"INSIDE, IT WAS MONSTROUSLY LAVISH. MRS. QUINCH IS AN INCREDIBLY RICH OLD LADY WITH MORE MONEY THAN LEGS."

ANOTHER *SCONE*, MISS PULGER?

"LATER, AS THE MEGA-PALACE DRIFTED AMONG THE STARS, I THOUGHT ABOUT *WAR* AND *RICH PEOPLE* AND ALL THE UTTERLY FANTASTIC THINGS THAT HAD, LIKE, *HAPPENED* TO ME..."

LIKE... WAR, AND RICH PEOPLE, AND...

"...ALL AT ONCE I *UNDERSTOOD* JUST *WHY* IT IS THAT MEN *FIGHT* EACH OTHER.

" I SUDDENLY SAW THE *ANSWER* TO ALL THIS *SENSELESS VIOLENCE* THAT AFFLICTS US'

"BUT, LIKE, I DIDN'T WRITE IT DOWN OR ANYTHING...

"AND, LIKE, Y'KNOW HOW IT IS — NEXT MORNING I HAD TOTALLY FORGOTTEN WHAT IT *WAS*, MAN."

The End

MR WALDO 'D.R.' DOBBS AND MR ERNEST ERROL QUINCH
1984 INTER-GALACTIC TENNIS TOURNAMENT
MEN'S DOUBLES CHAMPIONS.

DIPTHONK 5

D.R. & QUINCH	v	THE REST OF THE UNIVERSE	
SETS	2	SETS	0
GAMES	5	GAMES	0
POINTS	30	POINTS	0

2000 AD STAR LASER SCAN

MY NAME IS **WALDO 'D.R.' DOBBS.** ME AND MY FRIEND **ERNEST ERROL QUINCH** ARE, LIKE, TWO COLLEGE STUDENTS WHO HAVE ALL THESE AMAZINGLY HUMOROUS ADVENTURES.

THIS IS WHAT WE, LIKE, LOOK LIKE.

KLIK!

THIS IS THE STORY OF OUR MOST **INCREDIBLY STRANGE** STORY EVER.

WHAT I **MEAN** IS, THIS IS **NOT** OUR MOST INCREDIBLY STRANGE STORY EVER — THIS IS THE **STORY** OF OUR MOST INCREDIBLY STRANGE STORY EVER.

KLIK!

THIS **STORY,** MAN... I.E., THE INCREDIBLY **STRANGE** STORY MENTIONED ABOVE... IS CALLED **'D.R. AND QUINCH GO TO HOLLYWOOD'**

BUT, LIKE, **THIS** STORY, WHICH YOU ARE READING **NOW** — THIS IS JUST, LIKE, THE STORY **BEFORE** THAT STORY.

KLIK!

ANYWAY, TO CUT A LONG STORY SHORT...

FLAAAASSHH!

...IT BEGAN IN THE **UNITED GALAXIES OMNIBUS DEPOT...**

2000 A.D.
Credit Card:
SCRIPT ROBOT
ALAN MOORE
ART ROBOT
ALAN DAVIS
LETTERING ROBOT
STEVE POTTER
COMPU·73©

FASTPHOTOZ

D.R. & QUINCH
GO TO HOLLYWOOD
PROLOGUE

...NOT TILL *TONIGHT*!!

TONIGHT, A *DREAM* IS COMING *TRUE* FOR THIS *SHELL OF A MAN* THAT YOU SEE BEFORE YOU!

AFTER *TEN YEARS* OF *WRITER'S BLOCK*, I FINALLY CAME UP WITH AN *IDEA*! I GOT THE SCRIPT *RIGHT HERE*!!

LOOK OUT, HOLLYWOOD! TORQUETTO JUBBLI'S COMING BACK!

TEN YEARS OF *MISERY* AND *ILLNESS*! TEN LONG *YEARS*!! BUT DID I *GIVE UP*? I DID *NOT*!!

BECAUSE I *KNEW* THAT *ONE DAY*, I'D WALK INTO *C.B.'s* OFFICE, AND I'D SAY...

AK.

UH.

SLUUMPP!

HE'S TOTALLY *DEAD*, MAN.

WHAT AN AMAZINGLY TRAGIC THING TO HAPPEN TO HIM AT, LIKE, THIS STAGE OF HIS CAREER.

HEY, MAN, YOU KNOW WHAT? WE ARE NOT EVEN GONNA LOOK INSIDE THIS INCREDIBLE OLD GUY'S *POCKETS* TO SEE IF HE WAS TELLIN' THE TRUTH ABOUT THOSE *TICKETS*...

BECAUSE WHETHER IT WAS TRUE OR *NOT*, IT WAS, LIKE, HIS *DREAM*, MAN.

AND WE HAVE TO, LIKE, LET IT DIE *WITH* HIM.

LIKE... *R.I.P.*, T.J.

C'MON, C'MON! THEY GOTTA BE HERE SOME- WHERE!

YAHAAAAA!!!

NEXT PROG: *THAT'S ENTERTAINMENT??*

THERE ARE PLACES THAT ARE AWESOME... THERE ARE PLACES THAT ARE TOTALLY AWESOME... AND THEN THERE IS HOLLYWOOD.

HOLLYWOOD IS TOTALLY INCREDIBLY AWESOME, MAN.

2000 A.D.
Credit Card:
SCRIPT ROBOT
ALAN MOORE
ART ROBOT
ALAN DAVIS
LETTERING ROBOT
STEVE POTTER
COMPU·73ε

BY A STUPENDOUS GALACTIC COINCIDENCE, THERE WAS ALSO A HOLLYWOOD ON EARTH, WHICH WAS, LIKE, THIS COMPLETELY WORTHLESS SCUMBALL PLANET THAT ME AND QUINCH DESTROYED ONE TIME.

THIS ISN'T THAT HOLLYWOOD. THIS IS A DIFFERENT HOLLYWOOD.

MY, LIKE, STUPID FRIEND QUINCH AND MYSELF HAD COME TO HOLLYWOOD USING TICKETS BORROWED FROM MR. TORQUETTO JUBBLI, WHO IS THIS AMAZING BUT DEAD GUY THAT WE KNOW.

IT WAS A PLANET OF WASTED LIVES AND SHATTERED DREAMS, WHERE THE LITTLE FISH GOT EATEN...

WHA..?

UULLPPP!

...AND ONLY THE VICIOUS, BRUTAL AND EVIL SHARKS SURVIVED...

...SO, LIKE, WE HAD A REALLY FANTASTIC TIME, MAN, SPEAKING PERSONALLY.

D.R. & QUINCH
GO TO HOLLYWOOD
Part 1

HOLLYWOOD IS A *JUNGLE*, MAN, AND THERE ARE ONLY *FOUR RULES*.

THE FIRST RULE IS TO GET YOURSELF *NOTICED*...

SHUDDRROOON!!!

THE SECOND RULE IS TO IMPRESS PEOPLE WITH YOUR *GOOD TASTE* AND *FORCEFUL PERSONALITY*...

I WANT FIFTEEN *EMPEROR LOBSTERS*, MAN. AND I WANT THEM ALL WEARING LITTLE KNITTED *WAIST-COATS*... IN *PRUSSIAN BLUE*.

I HAVE, LIKE, *TOTALLY FORGOTTEN* WHAT THE *THIRD* AND *FOURTH* RULES ARE, MAN.

WHO *IS* THAT ODDLY CHARISMATIC YOUNG MAN?

OH, *HIM*? HE'S... UH... I *THINK* HE'S A FRIEND OF R.B.'S. *EVERYBODY'S* TALKING ABOUT HIM!

HEY, MAN, WHAT *IS* THIS *GARBAGE*? THESE WAISTCOATS ARE *CERULEAN* BLUE!

WHY, *HELLO* THERE!

OH, *COOK*! *G.D.* IS GOING OVER TO *SPEAK* TO HIM! HE MUST *KNOW* HIM!

I'M *G.D.* WHAT'S THE MATTER? HAVING TROUBLE WITH THE *FOOD*?

NO, MAN, BUT I'M HAVING AN INCREDIBLY VAST AMOUNT OF TROUBLE WITH THE FOOD'S *WAISTCOATS!*

WE'LL FIRE THE CHEF, SIR...

SEE THAT YOU *DO!* NOW, CLEAR THIS MESS AWAY AND ALLOW ME TO BUY SOME *REAL* FOOD FOR MR... UH... ER...

D.R., MAN.

OF *COURSE!* FOR *D.R.!*

AFTER THAT, THINGS HAPPENED WITH ASTOUNDING RAPIDITY...

HEY, C.K.! LISTEN...FRIEND OF *G.D.*'S... LEGENDARY FILM...*MARLON* OR *BURT*...

WOW! HEY, MARLON, LISTEN: FRIEND OF G.D.'S... LEGENDARY FILM... I HEAR IT'S *YOU* OR *BURT*...

WHUNH?

ME UH BUHRT, HUNH?

YOU MEAN, YOUR AGENT HASN'T *HEARD* ANYTHING YET? *GEE!* I GUESS THE PART MUST HAVE GONE TO *BURT*...

UH *YUH?* MUHBE I DUHN'T *LIKE* THAT!

PSST! I HEAR MARLON'S PRETTY ANGRY ABOUT BURT GETTING THE PART IN G.D.'S FRIEND D.R.'S NEW PICTURE...

YOUR CHOCOLATE-COATED *ANT'S BRAINS,* SIR.

FORGET IT, MAN. I AIN'T HUNGRY ANYMORE.

GLOOP!

HEY!

I GET THAT PUHT IN YUH PICHUH, Y'UNNERSTUHN?

YOU HEAR *THAT?* *MARLON* IS MAKING HIS *FIRST FILM* IN *FIVE YEARS!!*

INSTANT MEGA-BOX OFFICE! I GOTTA HAVE A PIECE OF THE *ACTION!* LET ME *FINANCE* THIS FILM...

NO! LET ME!

"SOMETIMES, MAN, IT IS AN INCREDIBLY LONELY LIFE BEING A BRILLIANT YOUNG HOLLYWOOD FILM MOGUL. YOU BECOME, LIKE, TOTALLY SHUT AWAY FROM YOUR PUBLIC..."

YO! SERVANT! SWITCH ON THE FORCE-FIELD, MAN.

"...BUT, LIKE, SINCE MOST OF THE PUBLIC ARE COMPLETE **MUDHEADS**, THIS IS NOT A MAJOR PROBLEM, AS I SEE IT."

SCHRRAAZZZZATT!

"WHAT **WAS** A MAJOR PROBLEM, MAN, WAS THIS TOTALLY UNREADABLE **SCRIPT** THAT I WAS, LIKE, SUPPOSED TO BE MAKING A FILM OUT OF.

"IN FACT, MAN, THIS WAS A PROBLEM OF MIND-LIQUEFYING MAJORNESS.

"THE SCRIPT HAD BEEN WRITTEN BY THIS LEGENDARY DEAD GUY THAT WE KNOW, AND THERE WERE ABOUT **FIFTY-ELEVEN-HUNDRED PAGES** OF IT.

"OF THIS, **EIGHT WORDS** WERE COMPLETELY READABLE.

"THESE WERE 'ORANGES', IN THE TITLE, AND "CLOSE THE CURTAINS, GEOFFREY, I'M AMPHIBIOUS", WHICH WAS RIGHT AT THE END.

"TO BE PERFECTLY **FRANK**, MAN, I WASN'T EVEN 100% SURE ABOUT 'AMPHIBIOUS'.

"AS IF THIS TOTALLY ILLEGIBLE SCRIPT WAS NOT BAD ENOUGH, I ALSO HAD THIS TOTALLY INCOMPREHENSIBLE LEADING MAN, MAN."

MR. DOBBS? MY BOY *MARLON* WANTS TO SEE THE *SCRIPT!*

UH WUNNUH SEETHUH *SCRUP!*

HEY, MAN! THE ACTORS AREN'T SUPPOSED TO SEE THE SCRIPT TILL *OPENING* NIGHT!

THIS IS AN INCREDIBLY STRANGE SHOW-BIZ *SUPERSTITION* THAT I ONCE HEARD.

GIMMUH THUH SCRUP!

UH, LOOK, MAN ... IF THERE'S ANYTHING YOU DON'T *LIKE*, WE CAN *CHANGE* IT.

I AM, LIKE, *TOTALLY FLEXIBLE* AT THIS STAGE.

S'MUSSERPUSS.

SUHBESS SCRUPHUH YEVUH RHUD!

YOU HEAR *THAT?* MARLON SAYS IT'S A *MASTER-PIECE!*

HE SAYS IT'S THE BEST SCRIPT HE'S *EVER READ!*

OH, *MARLON* ... COULD YOU DO A *SCENE* FOR US, HEART-FACE?

YEAH, MARLON, READ US SOMETHING OUT!

UH, HEY, MARLON— LISTEN, MAN, I DUNNO WHETHER YOU *SHOULD* ...

YUH, UHKAY. UHL READYUH UHBIDDUH THUH SCRUP.

QUIET, EVERYBODY!

WOW! MARLON SAYS IT'S *OKAY!* HE'LL READ US A BIT OF THE *SCRIPT!*

THIS **CHEQUE** IS TO ENSURE THAT IT **REMAINS** A SECRET.

HEY, MAN, MUM'S THE WORD!

AS MARLON'S MANAGER, I FEEL HONOUR BOUND TO TELL YOU WHAT YOU'VE PROBABLY ALREADY **GUESSED**...

MR. DOBBS, MARLON IS **TOTALLY UNABLE** TO **READ** OR **WRITE**. SINCE NO ONE CAN UNDERSTAND A WORD HE SAYS ANYWAY, THIS FACT HAS REMAINED A **SECRET**.

GLAD TO HEAR IT. Y'KNOW, IF IT WASN'T FOR MARLON'S CHARISMA HE'D STILL BE SERVING HYPER-PIZZAS IN THE STUDIO CANTEEN.

THIS PICTURE WILL DO HIM GOOD. WHERE DID YOU SAY IT WAS **SET** EXACTLY?

UH, WELL, MAN, DOES THIS WORD LOOK LIKE '**SANDWICH**' OR '**SUBMARINE**' TO YOU?

'SUBMARINE'.

RIGHT! SO, LIKE, IT'S SET ON A SUBMARINE, AND NOT ON A SANDWICH AS YOU MAY HAVE PREVIOUSLY IMAGINED, MAN.

I SEE. AND HOW WOULD YOU **DESCRIBE** THE FILM?

"HOW **COULD** I ADEQUATELY DESCRIBE THIS FILM, MAN? IT HAD AN **UNREADABLE** SCRIPT, AND AN **INCOHERENT LEADING MAN** WHO WAS ALSO, LIKE, **TOTALLY ILLITERATE!**"

"I DECIDED TO BE BRIEF AND HONEST.."

IT'S A DISASTER MOVIE, MAN.

NEXT PROG: **THE TOWERING ORANGES!**

"THERE ARE **SOME** PEOPLE, MAN, WHO THINK THAT LIFE AS A BRILLIANT YOUNG HOLLYWOOD **FILM MOGUL** IS, LIKE, ONE LONG PARADE OF **GLAMOUR** AND **NOVELTY**.

"THESE PEOPLE, MAN, ARE STUNNINGLY WRONG.

"WHAT I SAY TO THESE PEOPLE, MAN, IS THIS: I SAY, 'HEY MAN!'"

"THEY SAY, 'WHAT?'"

"I SAY, 'YOU ARE STUNNINGLY **WRONG**, MAN. THIS JOB, MAN, IS, IN FACT, SKULL-CRUNCHINGLY **DIFFICULT!'**"

"FOR ONE THING, I HAD AN **ASTOUNDING** AMOUNT OF DIFFICULTY WITH **MARLON**, WHO WAS, LIKE, MY **LEADING MAN**, MAN.

"MARLON WAS, LIKE, TOTALLY UNABLE TO READ, WRITE OR TALK PROPERLY. BRAVELY, HE REFUSED TO LET THIS INTERFERE WITH HIS LEGENDARY ACTING CAREER, MAN."

GUMMUH' VUH NUH' DUH?

"ALSO, MAN, WE HAD TEETHING PROBLEMS WITH THE **SCRIPT**. IT HAD BEEN WRITTEN BY THIS TOTALLY ILLITERATE **DEAD** GUY THAT WE KNOW, AND WAS **PHYSICALLY IMPOSSIBLE** TO READ.

"SO, LIKE, SINCE I DIDN'T HAVE THE SLIGHTEST IDEA WHAT THE STORY WAS ABOUT, I JUST ORDERED A LOT OF STUFF THAT WAS SORT OF **USEFUL-LOOKING**..."

SIXTEEN THOUSAND ORANGES...

SIXTEEN THOUSAND ORANGES!

"I **KNEW** WE'D DEFINITELY NEED THOSE ORANGES, SINCE THE TITLE OF THIS TOTALLY OUTRAGEOUS MASTERPIECE HAD "ORANGES" IN IT.

"IT ALSO HAD SOME OTHER WORDS, BUT YOUR GUESS IS AS GOOD AS MINE, MAN.

"MY OTHER BIG DIFFICULTY WAS WITH MARLON'S **MANAGER**..."

MR. DOBBS, I'M STARTING TO HAVE **SERIOUS WORRIES** ABOUT THIS **FILM**...

HEY MAN, I KNOW **EXACTLY** WHAT YOU MEAN.

I MEAN, WHAT'S IT ALL **ABOUT?** WHAT DO ALL THESE **NUNS** AND **FLAMINGOES** HAVE TO DO WITH ANYTHING?

HEY MAN, THIS IS **SYMBOLISM!!** THE NUNS AND FLAMINGOES ARE TOTALLY **VITAL** TO THE **PLOT!**

YOU SEE, THE **NUNS** ARE, LIKE, A SYMBOL OF **HAPPINESS**, MAN, WHILE THE FLAMINGOES REPRESENT SOMETHING INCREDIBLY UNUSUAL THAT I HAVE, LIKE, **FORGOTTEN** ABOUT.

AND WHAT DO ALL THE PILES OF **DECOMPOSING FISH** REPRESENT?

HEY MAN, THEY DON'T REPRESENT NOTHIN'. THEY'RE JUST FOR **COMIC RELIEF.**

HMMM. I DON'T **KNOW**, MR. DOBBS...

AS MARLON'S MANAGER, I'M VERY CONCERNED ABOUT HIM WORKING IN CONDITIONS LIKE THESE...

SOME OF THIS EQUIPMENT LOOKS DISTURBINGLY **DANGEROUS**, AND I DON'T LIKE THE WAY YOU'VE GOT THOSE SIXTEEN THOUSAND ORANGES JUST PILED UP OVER THERE...

HEY MAN, I AM OBSERVING **RIGOROUS SAFETY REGULATIONS!**

HEY! I GOT IT, MAN!

MARLON! *SOB* OH *NO!* THERE *HAS* TO BE A WAY TO *SAVE* HIM!

A WAY TO SAVE *MARLON??*

MARLON? DON'T BE *RIDICULOUS,* MAN! MARLON'S JUST BEEN CRUSHED BY ABOUT THREE HUNDRED TONS OF *ORANGES.*

NO, WHAT I MEAN IS, I *GOT A TITLE FOR THE FILM!*

"*SOMETHING SOMETHING ORANGES SOMETHING*"! DON'T YOU *SEE?*

I GOT THE IDEA WHEN YOU SHOUTED OUT JUST BEFORE THAT BRAIN-SQUEEZINGLY HUGE MOUNTAIN OF FRUIT COLLAPSED..

GENTLEMEN, THIS FILM IS CALLED "*MIND THE ORANGES, MARLON!*"

AND, LIKE, IT'S *MORE* THAN JUST A FILM! IT'S A *TRIBUTE* TO A GREAT STAR WHO IS, LIKE NO LONGER *WITH* US...

...MAINLY BECAUSE HE'S, LIKE UNDER ALL THOSE *ORANGES* OVER *THERE,* MAN.

S'RIGHT.

IT'S GOT *EVERYTHING,* MAN! IT'S GOT *TRAGEDY, HUMAN INTEREST* AND ALL *KINDS* OF STUPEFYINGLY INTERESTING STUFF LIKE THAT. MAN, THIS PICTURE COULD BE THE *BIGGEST BIGGIE* IN THE WHOLE OF *BIGDOM!*

GRRRRRR!

NOW, DON'T BE AFRAID TO GIVE ME YOUR GUT-LEVEL REACTION WITH REGARD TO THIS ONE, MEN...

NEXT PROG: **THE LAST PICTURE SHOW?**

D.R. & QUINCH

GO TO HOLLYWOOD
PART 4

DIRECT FROM THE CENTRAVIAN FILM FESTIVAL...

2000 A.D.
Credit Card:
SCRIPT ROBOT
ALAN MOORE
ART ROBOT
ALAN DAVIS
LETTERING ROBOT
STEVE POTTER
COMPU-73E

BARRY NORMAL HERE AT THE CENTRAVIAN FILM FESTIVAL, TALKING TO ONE OF THE FESTIVAL'S MOST **EXPLOSIVE** NEW TALENTS. POET, PHILOSOPHER, CINEMATIC GENIUS...ENIGMA, LEGEND, COLLEGE STUDENT, SAINT IN HUMAN FORM... **WALDO 'D.R.' DOBBS!**

D.R., YOUR NEW MOTION PICTURE—**"MIND THE ORANGES, MARLON!"**—HAS BECOME A LEGEND IN THE INDUSTRY, SCOOPING FIFTEEN 'DOSSER' AWARDS...

...AND YET HOLLYWOOD HAS **OSTRACIZED** YOU. WHY IS THIS?

HEY, MAN, YOU ARE TALKING TO THE VICTIM OF AN AWESOMELY MONSTROUS **SMEAR CAMPAIGN.**

NEVERTHELESS, ISN'T IT TRUE THAT YOUR **LEADING MAN** ACTUALLY **DIED** DURING FILMING?

IT WAS **NATURAL CAUSES,** MAN.

SURELY, BEING **CRUSHED** BENEATH **SIXTEEN THOUSAND ORANGES** HARDLY QUALIFIES AS NATURAL CAU—YURPP!'

SKRRUNCH!

N-NO... AAARGHHH!'

...UNHHH...

...OVER TO YOU IN THE STUDIO, CLIVE...

THANKS, BARRY.

"MIND THE ORANGES, MARLON!" ...IS IT A *CINEMATIC SOLILOQUY* OF *CITRUS SIGNIFICANCE?* OR A *FILM-NOIR FRUIT COCKTAIL* OF *FAIR-DINKUM FANTASMAGORIA?*

FILMWEEK

WHO KNOWS, WHO CARES, AND IS ANYONE *REALLY* CLEVER ENOUGH TO CATCH ALL THE WITTY THINGS I SAY?

I DON'T KNOW. WHO DOES? NOT ME, NOT YOU— CERTAINLY NOT MY AUNT DORIS.

LET'S LOOK AT THE *FILM*...

"THE FILM IS PIQUANT AND PERPLEXING, A PAGEANT OF PICTORIAL PUZZLES. HERE WE HAVE A SCENE SHOWING SOME JOURNALISTS IN A FORCE-FIELD...

"...FOLLOWED BY A HARROWING DREAM SEQUENCE, WHERE WOMEN DRESSED AS *GIANT CRABS* WANDER AIMLESSLY ROUND A FILM SET.

"WHAT DOES IT *MEAN?* IS IT ABOUT *CONFUSION?* PERSONALLY, I'M NOT SURE. WHO IS?

"THE CAMERAWORK THROUGHOUT IS PLEASINGLY *POIGNANT*, AND YET, PARADOXICALLY, *PATHETIC.*

"DOBBS HAS CAREFULLY CONSTRUCTED EACH SCENE TO LOOK LIKE THE WORK OF A *LARGE, LUMBERING, BRAINLESS MONSTER* PLAYING WITH A CAMERA.

"AND THEN, OF COURSE, THERE'S **"THAT"** SCENE..."

"SIXTEEN THOUSAND ORANGES RAINING DOWN IN SLOW MOTION UPON A MEGA-STAR OF THE MOTION PICTURE INDUSTRY."

NNUHH! MMNUHH— MMNUHH!

A TRIUMPH OF TASTELESSNESS, A VICTORY FOR VULGARITY... OR JUST A LONG STRIP OF CELLULOID WITH LITTLE HOLES DOWN THE SIDE? LET'S ASK THE EXPERTS...

IF THAT PSYCHOTIC LITTLE RODENT SHOWS HIS FACE HERE AGAIN, I WILL PERSONALLY PULL HIS ARMS AND LEGS OFF!

AND THE SAME GOES FOR THE GUY WHO WROTE THE **SCRIPT**... **TORQUETTO JUBBLI!**

HE MAY HAVE BEEN A GREAT WRITER **ONCE**, BUT IF HE EVER COMES TO **HOLLYWOOD** AGAIN HE'S **A DEAD MAN!**

MILTON "C.B." MULTIBOON, STUDIO PRESIDENT.

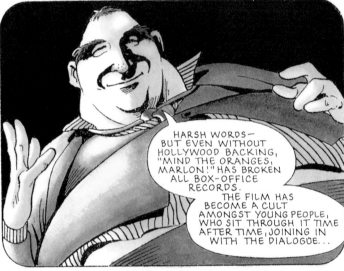

HARSH WORDS— BUT EVEN WITHOUT HOLLYWOOD BACKING, "MIND THE ORANGES, MARLON!" HAS BROKEN ALL BOX-OFFICE RECORDS. THE FILM HAS BECOME A CULT AMONGST YOUNG PEOPLE, WHO SIT THROUGH IT TIME AFTER TIME, JOINING IN WITH THE DIALOGUE...

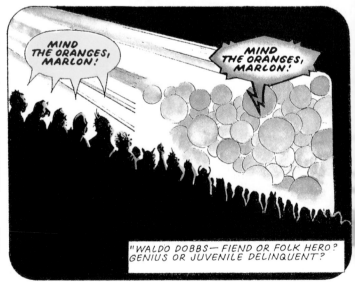

MIND THE ORANGES, MARLON!

MIND THE ORANGES, MARLON!

"WALDO DOBBS— FIEND OR FOLK HERO? GENIUS OR JUVENILE DELINQUENT?"

"ONE: NOBODY KNOWS WHERE HE IS.

"TWO: THE SAME GOES FOR THE BOX-OFFICE TAKINGS."

WELL... LIKE, HERE WE *ARE*, MAN.

BACK IN THE SAME PLACE WHERE WE SET OUT ON OUR BRAIN FRYINGLY PROFITABLE EXPLOITS.

THIS, TO ME, IS, LIKE, TOTALLY SIGNIFICANT.

AFTER ALL, IF WE HAD NOT COME TO THIS PLACE WE MIGHT NEVER HAVE MET THAT INCREDIBLE OLD DEAD GUY, *T.J.* ... I REMEMBER HIM LIKE IT WAS ONLY FOUR WEEKS AGO, MAN. WE MET HIM RIGHT ABOUT...

...HERE.

HEY, MAN, I AM, LIKE, COMPLETELY *OUTRAGED!*

THIS DEAD GUY HAS BEEN *LYING HERE* FOR AN ENTIRE *MONTH* SINCE WE LEFT HIM!

DIDN'T ANYBODY THINK TO CLEAR HIM *UP??* I DUNNO, MAN. SOME *PEOPLE...*

I AM, LIKE, TOTALLY RESOLVED TO WRITE A LETTER TO THE *SANITATION DEPARTMENT.* HERE IS WHAT I WILL SAY, MAN — "DEAR DIRTBAGS..."

UH.

AK.

"'...C.B.! IT'S ME, *TORQUETTO JUBBLI*! I'M *BACK*, AND HAVE I GOT A *SCRIPT* FOR *YOU!*'"

THAT'S WHAT I'LL SAY TO HIM. HEH HEH...

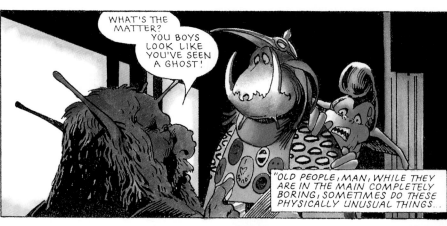

WHAT'S THE MATTER? YOU BOYS LOOK LIKE YOU'VE SEEN A GHOST!

"OLD PEOPLE, MAN, WHILE THEY ARE IN THE MAIN COMPLETELY BORING, SOMETIMES DO THESE PHYSICALLY UNUSUAL THINGS..."

"IN THIS INSTANCE, AN ASTONISHING OLD DEAD GUY HAD SUDDENLY COME OUT OF HIS INCREDIBLY WEIRD *COMA*— COMPLETING A SENTENCE HE'D STARTED A MONTH AGO."

...ANYWAY, THANKS FOR LISTENING TO MY STORY, BOYS.

I'LL TAKE MY *MANUSCRIPT* BACK IF I MAY. THIS SCRIPT IS GOING TO MAKE MY FORTUNE WHEN I GET BACK TO *HOLLYWOOD!*

HEH HEH. I CAN'T *WAIT* TO SEE THE LOOK ON OLD C.B.'S FACE...

HEH HEH HEH

HEY... THAT'S SHOWBIZ, MAN.

The End (Man)

89

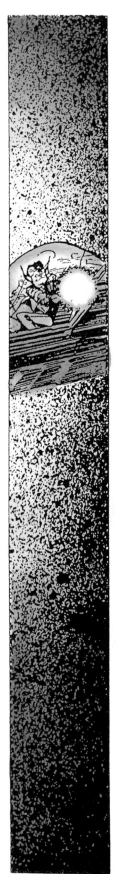

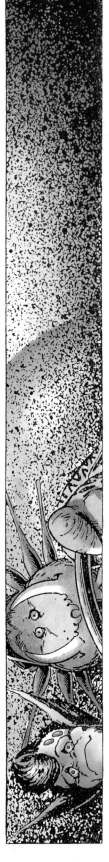